NNS

"Don't worry, Herb, you don't have to eat it."

NNS

"Look! We're shopping not sightseeing!"

"Okay, Okay! I get the message!"

"I *told* you we shouldn't have pretended we weren't home!"

"Where's your sense of humor?!?"

"He kin do every trick in th' whole world, but he won't beg! He's got PRIDE!"

"Next time, don't promise him leftovers!"

"Now, Mommyduke! Bark real loud!"

"Phil, I think he wants a refill on the lemonade!"

"Don't tell *him* we're going to have s-t-e-a-k!"

"He worries about me."

"Well, then, would you get lost for 50 cents??"

"Don't tell *him* you burned it . . .
I can't stand to see a dog cry!"

"Dottie, call the police station and see if Cave's meat market reported a robbery!"

"Stop bawling! We'll get him out of there if we have to cut down the tree!"

"I wish he'd stop answering the door! First thing you know, we won't have any friends left!"

"If you're so tired, take a nap!"

"His name is Marmaduke, but he's called everything *but* that!"

"Careful! I think that car ahead
is going to *do* something!"

"Shut up! It's Saturday!"

"This is delicious! You sure you didn't get confused and serve us Marmaduke's dinner?"

"When I pull your tail, bark.
The horn's broken."

"I told you he knows what b-a-t-h spells!"

"Mommie threatened to replace him with a garbage disposal!"

"Should we go out and come in the back way?"

"How'd he find out we were taking him for his shot?"

"It says you're sweet, gentle, kind, considerate . . . It must be out of order!"

"Don't tell *me* how to hang it! *You're* the one who knocked it down!"

"When are we gonna get a Society for the Prevention of Cruelty to Humans?"

"Phil, you should feel honored that you're the only one he likes to go for walks with!"

"Me an' Mommyduke have been kicked out of better places than this!"

"NOT UNDER THE COUCH ! ! !"

"I shudder when I think he's storing up energy each moment he lies there!"

"If we got rid of *him,* we would . . ."

". . . Sure miss him!"

"Anyone seen my other shoe?"

"For Pete's sake, go stare at somebody else for a while!"

"Now you look just like one o' the Beatles!"

"One well done, one medium, one rare, and eight raw!"

"Heads, he gets the floor and I get the couch
. . . Tails, I get the floor and he . . ."

"WHATSA MATTER? CAN'TCHA READ?!"

"That's YOU barking, Marmaduke!
I just taped it!"

"Beat it! You're ruining the sales pitch!"

"I'll bet he's having a wonderful dream!"

"But where are the antlers?"

"You want him moved, YOU move him!"

"He *did too* make a touchdown . . . and we'll *prove* it as soon as we find the football!"

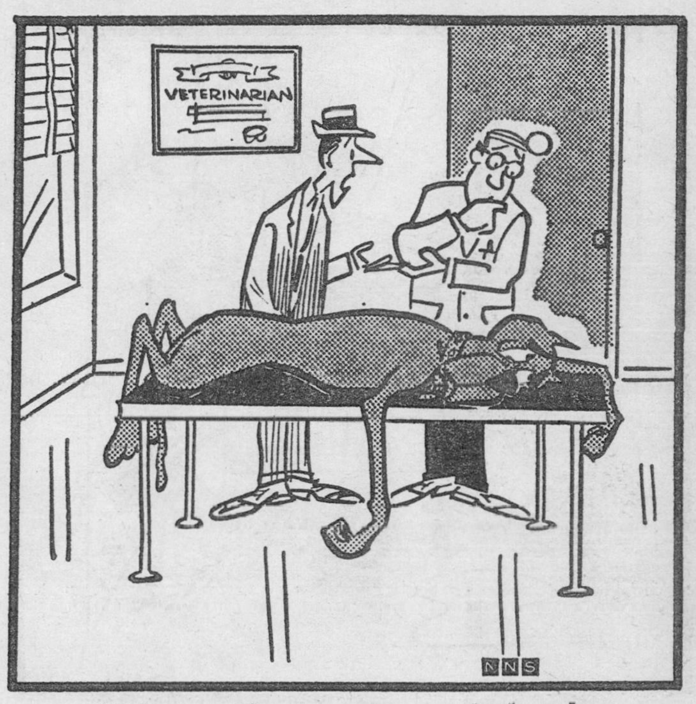

"He's been like this ever since he lost the blue ribbon at the dog show!"

"How *did* you know Marmaduke did it?"

12-15

WOOF
NNS

"He's playing staredown with the
new dog on the block!"

"What'll you bet it's the Welcome Wagon?"

"Phil, we have a problem!"

"That's silly! How can he be dangerous if he doesn't bite?"

"Well, you must have done SOMETHING that annoyed him!"

"Okay, so he's offering me his most prized possession . . . What's the catch?"

"Let's move to an apartment where they don't allow dogs!"

"Let's face it. His bark is getting stronger and your horn is getting weaker!"

"It'll be kinda crowded, but come on in!"

"He didn't like the way you growled in first gear!"

"Beats me how they could have *anything* to throw away with *that* mutt around!"

"Okay, *you* can have the sandwich if you'll just let *me* have the apple and cheese!"

"It was a swell party, Mom, 'til Marmaduke had a second helping *three* times!"

"Deciding on a snack . . . or just defrosting the refrigerator?"

"That's strange! He doesn't usually make such a fuss over people!"

"It's funny, Fred, but we haven't seen *one* dog all day!"

"You're wasting talent . . .
Dreamboat's not home!"

"Go easy with that stuff, Dottie!
It's *loaded* with energy!"

"Anybody seen my new hat?"

"Call him off, Mister, or I'll book you for assault, too!"

"He flunked obedience training again!"

"It's strange . . . When he handles complaints, there aren't any!"

"Honest, Mr. Snyder, I won't throw any more snowballs at you!"

“I think he’s trying to *tell* you
something, Phil!”

"Don't try to tell me that was an *accident!*"

"Practicing for the Olympics?"

"Heads, we watch the news—tails, Lassie!"

"Look, Mommy! Mommyduke found my bubble gum!"

"I guess *he* didn't care for the
veal scallopini either!"

"*Nobody* could get me out on a night like this!"

"Nobody???"

"At least take him around the block, Snyder. He won't *move* until you do!"

"I'd like to see him dig *that one* up!"

"Go 'way! I can wash my *own* ears!"

"I dropped a ham bone in the disposal."

"Relax, Harry, he's just waiting for the bone."

"It's OK, lady . . . He's an honorary Boy Scout!"

"I'll have a peanut butter sandwich,
but my friend here wants steak!"

"I didn't find my cuff links, but I found a ham bone, a T-bone, and a porterhouse!"

"Madam, just give me my case and
I'll never come back!"

"Why did you have to lean against it?"

"How do you know I didn't brush my teeth?!?"

"Br-r-r-rother! He'll *never* get the last bark here!"

"You mean the dog pound *refused* him???"

"Somebody ought to enlighten him about dog food, stew beef, and hamburger!"

"Oh, oh! Here comes trouble!"

"All right, all right! We'll put him through as a dependent!"

"Oh, I'm sorry! He thought it was his master!"

"How about a tablecloth, Dottie?"

"We have to make a decision! We either have friends . . . or HIM!"

"You'll serve the baked potatoes and salad while I carve WHAT roast?"

Oh, Brother, they'll NEVER believe this accident report!

"Mommie, how come dogs kin bite
mailmen but little boys can't?"

"Remember, Joe, radiate confidence!"

"Please keep him out of here, Mr. Winslow!
He's taught all my parakeets to bark!"

"Don't worry, Grace, he doesn't like tuna fish sandwiches!"

"If I don't show him the way home, we'll be out here all night!"

"*Now* call me a pipsqueak!"

"Watch it, Phil! He's had a bad day!"

"I did not say I *had been* leading a dog's life . . . I said I wish I *could!*"

"You send us outside to help Daddy an' he sends us in to help you an' you send us outside to help Daddy an' he sends . . ."

"I said I'd take you for a *walk* . . . not a *run!*"

"Planning your own forest, Winslow?"

"NO THANKS!!"

"It's the Winslows and they've got You-Know-Who with them!"

"We live next door. You'll see a *lot* of Marmaduke!"

"Our picnic's in Marmaduke's stomach!"

"For once, we'll have a quiet dinner . . .
I tied him to the car!"

NNS

"Stop calling him a nincompoop! When he finds out what it means, you've *had* it!"

"I hate to think what would happen if you dropped one!"

"Just because we wouldn't let him
in with muddy feet!"

"He's even getting to *look* like a hamburger!"

"Now *there's* a picture for your picture window!"

FOR SALE
FOR SALE
FOR SALE
NNS